GRADE 2

The 2005–2007 Syllabus s[...]
requirements, especially th[...]
sight-reading. Attention sh[...]
Notices on the inside front c[...]
any changes.

The syllabus is obtainable from music retailers or from the Services Department, The Associated Board of the Royal Schools of Music, 24 Portland Place, London W1B 1LU, United Kingdom (please send a stamped addressed C5 (162mm × 229mm) envelope).

In exam centres outside the UK, information and syllabuses may be obtained from the Local Representative.

CONTENTS

Where appropriate, pieces in this volume have been checked with original source material and edited as necessary for instructional purposes. Fingering, phrasing, bowing, metronome marks and the editorial realization of ornaments (where given) are for guidance only; they are not comprehensive or obligatory.

DO NOT PHOTOCOPY © MUSIC

Alternative pieces for this grade

Music origination by Andrew Jones.
Cover by Økvik Design.
Printed in England by Caligraving Ltd, Thetford, Norfolk.

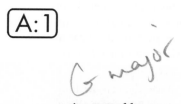

Papageno's Song
from *Die Zauberflöte*

Arranged by
Robert Spearing and Mary Cohen

MOZART

In Mozart's opera *Die Zauberflöte* (*The Magic Flute*) Papageno is a bird-catcher who accompanies a Javanese prince on a mission to rescue the daughter of the Queen of Night. The demisemiquaver figures in the right hand of the piano accompaniment at bb. 13–14 and 18–19 represent the sound of Papageno's panpipes.

Reproduced from *Superstart Violin*, Level 2, by permission of the publishers. All enquiries for this piece apart from the exams should be addressed to Faber Music Ltd, 3 Queen Square, London WC1N 3AU.

AB 3002

Menuet in G

BWV Anh. II 114

from *Clavierbüchlein vor Anna Magdalena Bach, 1725*

A:2

Arranged by
Edward Huws Jones

PEZOLD

In 1725 Johann Sebastian Bach (1685–1750) dedicated two keyboard suites to his wife Anna Magdalena, and they became the first entries in a little keyboard book belonging to her. The rest of the book seems to have been filled gradually over some years, with favourite pieces of Anna Magdalena's, compositions by her children, and pieces – including this one – by contemporary musicians such as Christian Pezold (1677–1733), who was probably a friend of the Bach family. The melody is graceful and flexible, but the underlying pulse – as in all dance music – needs to be rock-steady.

AB 3002

A:3

La morisque

Arranged by
Edward Huws Jones

SUSATO

The title *La morisque* has the same origins as the English 'morris dance': literally, music of the North African Moors. So think of this uncomplicated 16th-century tune as a lively morris dance, in a rollicking duple pulse. EHJ

© 2000 by Boosey & Hawkes Music Publishers Ltd
Reproduced from *The Early Music Fiddler* by permission. All enquiries for this piece apart from the exams should be addressed to Boosey & Hawkes Music Publishers Ltd, Aldwych House, 71-91 Aldwych, London WC2B 4HN.

AB 3002

Simple Gifts

B:1

Arranged by
Polly Waterfield and Louise Beach

ANON. AMERICAN

This well-known tune originates from the American Shaker society, a religious group that also made beautiful and simple wooden furniture. The American composer Aaron Copland (1900–90) used the tune in his ballet *Appalachian Spring*. It is also known as *Lord of the Dance*, after the adaptation by Sydney Carter (1915–2004). PW

AB 3002

Russischer Marsch
Op. 426

Arranged by
Edward Huws Jones

J. STRAUSS II

Johann Strauss II (1825–99) is famous for his waltzes but he also wrote polkas, marches and other pieces. *Russian March* needs to be played with panache: remember that Johann, as a young man, used to practise his violin in front of a full-length mirror so that he would look, as well as sound, like a star performer! EHJ

© Copyright 2001 by Boosey & Hawkes Music Publishers Ltd

Reproduced from *The Viennese Fiddler* by permission. All enquiries for this piece apart from the exams should be addressed to Boosey & Hawkes Music Publishers Ltd, Aldwych House, 71-91 Aldwych, London WC2B 4HN.

Moon Sprites

No. 7 from *The Enchanted Isle*

B:3

CARROLL

As we dance the dew doth fall,
Trip it, little urchins all.

John Lyly (*c.*1554–1606),
The Maydes Metamorphosis

Lightsome ♩ = *c.*126

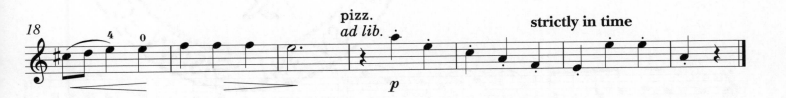

Walter Carroll (1869–1955) taught at the Royal Manchester College of Music before becoming one of the founding staff of the Northern School of Music. About the collection *The Enchanted Isle* he wrote: 'An island set in the blue expanse of ocean: the home of stately palms, of brilliant flowers, of exquisite living creatures: an inspiration to poet, artist and musician – such is the source from which these little sound-pictures were shaped in the mind of the composer.' The use of pizzicato in bb. 21–4 is optional.

AB 3002

C:1

Napoleon Crossing the Alps

Arranged by
Edward Huws Jones

ANON. IRISH

In this traditional Irish hornpipe the rhythm is paramount, as it is in all dance music. Each pair of quavers is played as a triplet, and the tempo should be fast enough to create a feeling of two beats in the bar. EHJ

Reproduced from *The Ceilidh Collection* by permission. All enquiries for this piece apart from the exams should be addressed to Boosey & Hawkes Music Publishers Ltd, Aldwych House, 71-91 Aldwych, London WC2B 4HN.

Wind Up

C:2

TIMOTHY KRAEMER

The title *Wind Up* suggests to me a playful and cheeky feel to the piece. This can be helped by exaggerating the offbeat accents and closely observing the dynamics. By contrast, the dolce passage should sound sweeter. TK

Timothy Kraemer has written a set of pieces in a similar vein called *Mood Swings*, in which the player is encouraged to 'act out' the mood of each piece.

C:3

Moderato

First movement from *Little Children's Suite*

Arranged by
Helena Dunicz-Niwińska and Maria Dziewulska

BAIRD

The Polish composer Tadeusz Baird (1928–81) began studying composition in Warsaw during World War II. *Little Children's Suite*, originally for piano, was written in 1954. The bowing symbols indicate the following:

- with the middle part of the bow
- with the lower part of the bow
- with the whole bow

Checklist of Scales and Arpeggios

Candidates and teachers may find this checklist useful in learning the requirements of the grade. Full details of the forms of the various requirements, including details of rhythms, starting notes and bowing patterns, are given in the syllabus and in the scale books published by the Board.

Grade 2

			separate bows						slurred					
									two quavers to a bow					
Major Scales	C Major	1 Octave	✓						✓					
	F Major	1 Octave	✓											
	G Major	2 Octaves	✓											
	A Major	2 Octaves	✓											
	B♭ Major	2 Octaves	✓											
Minor Scales (*melodic* or *harmonic*)	G Minor	1 Octave	✓						*two quavers to a bow* ✓					
	D Minor	1 Octave	✓											
	A Minor	1 Octave	✓											
Major Arpeggios	C Major	1 Octave	✓						*not applicable*					
	F Major	1 Octave	✓											
	G Major	2 Octaves	✓											
	A Major	2 Octaves	✓											
	B♭ Major	2 Octaves	✓											
Minor Arpeggios	G Minor	1 Octave	✓						*not applicable*					
	D Minor	1 Octave	✓											
	A Minor	1 Octave	✓											

A Tuneful Introduction to the 3rd position —
Neil Mackay

Superstudies Book 2. by Mary Cohen
Faber publication.

Elementary + Progressive Studies for violin
Book 2
Herbet Kinsey.

Support Material for ASSOCIATED BOARD Violin Exams

Recordings of Violin Exam Pieces 2005–2007

Recordings of all the pieces on the 2005–2007 violin syllabus. Each CD includes complete performances and playalong practice tracks.

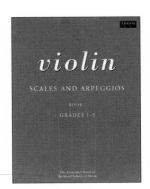

Scales and Arpeggios

In two volumes: Grades 1–5, Grades 6–8

Includes all the scales and arpeggios required at each grade.

Specimen Sight-Reading Tests

In two volumes: Grades 1–5, Grades 6–8

A selection of tests that demonstrate the technical level expected in the Associated Board's violin exams. The tests explore fully the parameters of each grade and provide excellent practice material for pupils.

Aural Training in Practice
Ronald Smith

In three volumes: Grades 1–3, Grades 4 & 5, Grades 6–8

Clear, structured guidance for candidates preparing for the aural tests in the Associated Board's practical exams. In addition to the many practice tests included, the books offer preparatory exercises and instruction.

Separate CD and cassette recordings also available

Available from all good music retailers

Containing nine pieces from the Associated Board's 2005–2007 violin syllabus, Grade 2, this album is indispensable to teachers and pupils alike.

- Three pieces from each of Lists A, B and C from the Grade 2 syllabus
- Meticulously edited and presented throughout
- Helpful footnotes and syllabus information
- Rich and varied repertoire from which to create an exciting programme for an exam or concert

ASSOCIATED BOARD
OF THE ROYAL SCHOOLS OF MUSIC

The Associated Board of the Royal Schools of Music is the world's leading provider of graded music exams and assessments. Each year over 600,000 candidates take our exams in more than 90 countries around the world.

ABRSM
PUBLISHING

The Associated Board of
the Royal Schools of Music
(Publishing) Limited

24 Portland Place
London W1B 1LU
United Kingdom

www.abrsmpublishing.co.uk

Oxford University Press is the sole worldwide sales agent and distributor for ABRSM Publishing.

ISBN 1-86096-473-7

9 781860 964732

Favourite Movements for Organ

A collection of beautiful music arranged by Colin Hand

Kevin Mayhew

ISBN 0-86209-594-8

Contents

HOW LOVELY ARE THY DWELLINGS
from REQUIEM

Johannes Brahms (1833-1897)

ALLEGRETTO from SYMPHONY No 3

Franz Schubert (1797-1828)

ADAGIO from CELLO CONCERTO

Edward Elgar (1857-1934)

ANDANTE CANTABILE from TRUMPET CONCERTO

Joseph Haydn (1732-1809)

HOMAGE MARCH from SIGURD JORSALFAR

Edvard Grieg (1843-1907)

BALLET No 2 from ORPHEUS

Christoph von Gluck (1714-1787)

GAVOTTE from SUITE No 3 in D

Johann Sebastian Bach (1685-1750)

ALLELUIA from EXULTATE JUBILATE

Wolfgang Amadeus Mozart (1756-1791)

PILGRIMS' CHORUS from TANNHÄUSER

Richard Wagner (1813-1883)

SLEEP SONG from HANSEL AND GRETEL

Engelbert Humperdinck (1854-1921)

SCHERZO from SYMPHONY No 5

Felix Mendelssohn (1809-1847)

2nd time D.C. al Fine
senza ripet.

VLTAVA from MA VLAST

Bedřich Smetana (1824-1884)

46

MINUET from SAMSON

George Frideric Handel (1685-1759)

cresc.

f

D.S.
senza ripet.

SYMPHONY and CHORUS
from COME YE SONS OF ART

Henry Purcell (1659-1695)

ANDANTE CON MOTO from SYMPHONY No 5

Ludwig van Beethoven (1770-1827)

LARGO from NEW WORLD SYMPHONY

Antonín Dvořák (1841-1904)

CUJUS ANIMAM from STABAT MATER

Gioachino Rossini (1792-1868)

BASSE-DANSE from CAPRIOL SUITE

Peter Warlock (1894-1930)